When the World Went Quiet

Written by Tia Martina

Illustrated by Kelly Ulrich

When the World Went Quiet

Distributed globally with Expanded Distribution by KDP.

ISBN Paperback: 978-0-9963668-5-4
ISBN E-Book: 978-0-9963668-6-1
Library of Congress Control Number: 2020943321

INSPIREBYTES OMNI MEDIA

Inspirebytes Omni Media LLC
PO Box 988
Wilmette, IL 60091

For more information, please visit www.inspirebytes.com.

This book is dedicated to everyone around the globe who works to protect the animals and nature that surround us. We both loved reading about the stories of animals returning to "human spaces" during the global pandemic of 2020. It reminded us that at this time in our global history it is increasingly important to focus on the preservation of wilderness and the protection of wildlife.

To that end, we have decided to donate 10% of all profits from the sale of this book to conservation efforts around the globe. By purchasing this book, you have helped give back in the hope of protecting our collective future.

Thank you,

Martin Kelly

One very different morning,
not quite so long ago...

the world woke up to silence
without a blanket of snow.

The quiet was from the machines
no longer on the roads.

The quiet was from the people staying safely in their homes.

This silence was something rare
we had never heard before,
and it became an invitation
for nature to explore.

In no time at all,
the animals began to show their faces
in backyards, on beaches,
and other unexpected places.

Foxes snuck into people's gardens
to romp, cavort, and play.

While goats munched on green grasses
instead of old, dry hay.

In the blue canals of Venice,
there were "tales" of dolphins swimming.

Whereas photos of Singapore's fountains
showed happy otters grinning.

The waterways ran clearer
than they had in thousands of days.

Now the fish swimming in them
could see the sun’s bright rays.

Giant elephants wandered slowly,
foraging for tasty treats.

Where they were joined by the spotted civet
on India’s empty streets.

Wild pumas roamed the streets in Chile,
near homes with fun new smells.

While monkeys played hide and seek together,
among Thailand's silent bells.

In Europe, wild boars caused havoc,
as they roamed freely through the towns.

Whereas the geese in Israel went to beaches to have a nice lie down.

Rats in New Orleans seemed to party,
as they gathered at night to play.

CITY
CANAL
2002
2014

But the capybara in Argentina
wandered in the middle of the day!

It seems the animals had decided
it was a good time to explore,
since their world was slightly bigger
than it had been just weeks before.

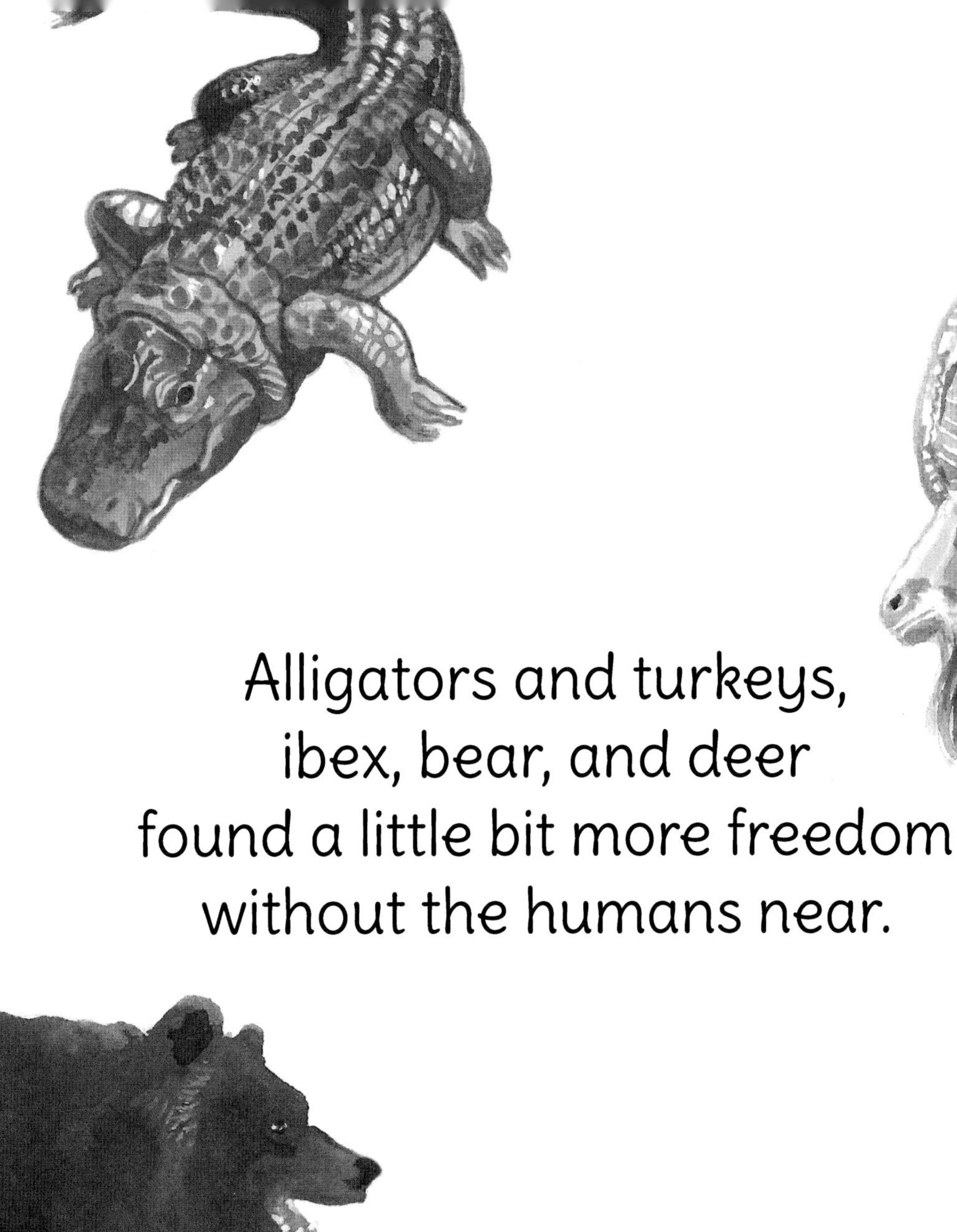

Alligators and turkeys,
ibex, bear, and deer
found a little bit more freedom
without the humans near.

So, while people helped each other
by staying safely in their homes...

nature showed up all around the world
to explore, play, and roam.

If the stories of the animals
brought a smile to your face,
perhaps it's time to consider
how we can share more space.

So, wherever you are,
and whatever you do,
think of how you can make room
for the animals, too.

SLOW DOWN
WILDLIFE CROSSING

About the Author

Tia Martina loves finding magic in everyday events. Whether it's from walks in the forest with her dogs or watching her bird eat from a bowl of spaghetti, she enjoys capturing (and writing about) the little moments that make life special and fun.

When Tia Martina is not creating new ideas and adventures, she likes to spend time with her friends, or can be found reading, making art, or listening to music. For more information, visit www.tiamartina.com.

About the Illustrator

Kelly Ulrich is an artist from the west coast of Canada, who likes painting so much she created a rain forest in her kitchen! When she's not busy dreaming up new children's stories, she can be found sipping a cup of tea in her backyard while watching nature, or working on her successful comic strip series on Instagram: "Nala, Dean & Vinny."

You can find Kelly on Instagram at: @kellyulrichartist.

A Note from Martina and Kelly

Hi! We hope you enjoyed reading about all the different animals in our book! It was fun for us to hear these amazing but true stories from around the world. The "tales" of dolphins in Venice's canals turned out to be false, but it made us happy to daydream about them swimming next to gondolas... and splashing them with their tails!

The world is full of so many wonderful animal and nature stories—maybe you'll hear a story you like and start daydreaming yourself about what's possible. To learn more about how people around the world are helping animals, visit **www.whentheworldwentquiet.com** for a list of resources we put together with our friends who work in conservation.

Made in the USA
Coppell, TX
30 January 2021

49236996R00031